CULL VOLUME FIVE

written by **GREG RUCKA**

art by **MICHAEL LARK**
with **TYLER BOSS**

colors by **SANTI ARCAS**

letters by **JODI WYNNE**

cover by **MICHAEL LARK**

edited by **DAVID BROTHERS**

publication design by **ERIC TRAUTMANN**

D0204422

Special thanks to **MICHAEL BROUND, OZ DONALD, MIRIAM FUCHS, KAYS KADAR,** and **MIKHAIL KISELGOF.**

FAMILY

FAMILY: Carlyle
DOMAIN: Western United States (west coast of Alaska contested with Vassalovka); Western Canada; Northern Canada.
Allied with Morray, Carragher, Bittner.
In conflict with Hock, Rausling, D'Souza, and Vassalovka.

JOHANNA CARLYLE
Acting Head
of Family.

MALCOLM CARLYLE
Patriarch of Family Carlyle; recovering from poisoning.

DR. BETHANY CARLYLE
Daughter of Malcolm Carlyle.

STEPHEN CARLYLE
Son of Malcolm Carlyle.

COMMANDER FOREVER CARLYLE
Family Carlyle Lazarus.

EVE
Next-generation Lazarus.

CARLYLE-AFFILIATED SERFS

ARTHUR COHN
Chief Family advisor.

COMMANDING GENERAL DIEGO VALERI
Carlyle supreme military commander.

GUNNERY SERGEANT MARISOL OCCAMPO
Dagger; Combat instructor to Carlyle Lazarus.

CORPORAL CASEY SOLOMON
Carlyle infantry soldier, hero of Duluth Campaign.

DR. MICHAEL BARRETT
Former Waste; Lifted in X+64 for medical aptitude.

JOE BARRETT
Former Waste; father of Michael Barrett.

BOBBIE BARRETT
Former Waste; Joe's spouse, Michael's mother.

SERÉ COOPER
Most popular anchor of Carlyle's entertainment/news programming.

FAMILY: Morray
DOMAIN: Mexico and Central America, portions of the Caribbean. **Member of Carlyle Bloc. In conflict with D'Souza and Hock.**

EDGAR MORRAY
Head of Family Morray.

JOACQUIM MORRAY
Family Morray Lazarus.

FAMILY: Armitage
DOMAIN: United Kingdom of Great Britain and Ireland-made-One. **Part of the Carlyle bloc. In conflict with Rausling and D'Souza.**

HRH THE DUKE OF LANCASTER EDWARD ARMITAGE
Head of Family Armitage.

SIR THOMAS HUSTON
Family Armitage Lazarus.

FAMILY: Bittner
DOMAIN: Canada (former provinces of Ontario, Quebec, Newfoundland & Labrador); Northern Europe/North Atlantic (Switzerland, Scandinavia), Germany. **Member of Carlyle bloc. In conflict with Hock and Rausling.**

SEVARA BITTNER
Head of Family Bittner.

SONJA BITTNER
Family Bittner Lazarus.

FAMILY: Hock
DOMAIN: Former United States, east of the Mississippi; portions of the Caribbean; portions of southeastern Canada. **Allied with Vassalovka, Rausling, and D'Souza. In conflict with Armitage, Carlyle, Bittner, Morray.**

DR. JAKOB HOCK
Head of Family; bitter enemy of Malcolm Carlyle.

FAMILY: Rausling
DOMAIN: Austria, Poland, portions of Central Europe, between Bittner-controlled Western Europe and Vassalovka-controlled Russia; Greece, excluding Meyers-Qasimi held Crete and Cyprus. **Member of Hock Coalition. In conflict with Armitage, Bittner, Carlyle, Morray.**

LUKA RAUSLING
Head of Family Rausling.

CAPTAIN CRISTOF MUELLER
Family Rausling Lazarus.

MICHAEL LARK

CULL CHAPTER ONE

April, X+65

APPROACHING TARGET...

...TEN SECONDS, STAND BY...

DAGGERS! STAND-BY!

...STAND-BY...

...STAND-BY...

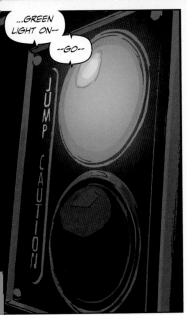

...GREEN LIGHT ON--

--GO--

JUMP CAUTION

--GO GO!

Graubünden Canton, Switzerland—
43KM due west of Davos
Alt: 11, 207 m

Family: Carlyle
Six weeks earlier

--REGAINED CONSCIOUSNESS DURING TRANSPORT--

nHnn

--THE WAY, GET *OUT* OF THE *WAY!*

Population [Family]:
4 [1 permanent]
Population [Serf]: 67

HOLD HER STEADY!

MICHAEL, HER *LEG!*

--SHE FOUGHT US THE WHOLE WAY, WE TRIED TO SEDATE HER BUT NOTHING TOOK--

INDUCTION TRIGGERS ARE *STILL* FIRING, AT LEAST WHAT'S *LEFT* OF THEM.

ON THREE, MICHAEL. ONE, TWO--

hnn
NHNNNH

FOR GOD'S SAKE, KEEP HER *STILL!*

--THREE.

NHHN
HNNnh

FOREVER. *FOREVER,* YOU'RE GOING TO BE OKAY--

gnNHn
HNNH

TWO MONTHS.

WHY SO LONG?

BECAUSE IN CASES LIKE THIS, EVERYTHING WE **DESIGNED** HER TO DO ACTUALLY WORKS **AGAINST** US.

WE DON'T WANT HER **HEALING** AN INCISION EVEN AS WE'RE **MAKING** IT.

IT'S TAKEN **TWO DAYS** JUST TO GET HER READY FOR SURGERY. WE'VE HAD TO RETARD HER TRANSCRIPTION FACTORS, MODIFY PLURIPOTENCY, DISABLE--

ZONE KAPPA

I GET IT.

Oh? THEN YOU **ALSO** UNDERSTAND THAT O FACILITATE **ALL** THIS WE'VE HAD TO TAKE HER OFF HER **MEDS?**

THEN WE HAVE TO **REINTRODUCE** THE DRUG REGIMEN--

THE **REPLACEMENT** LIMB IS EASY--IT'S NOT LIKE THERE'S A RISK OF **REJECTION**-- BUT WE **STILL** HAVE TO ACCOUNT FOR **PHYSICAL THERAPY.**

I NEED HER READY TO DEPLOY AGAIN IN FOUR WEEKS.

THAT'S NOT ENOUGH TIME, JO.

WE'RE AT **WAR,** BETH.

I NEED FOREVER IN THE **FIELD,** AND IT HAS TO BE SOON.

DO IT FOR YOUR FAMILY, **BIG** SISTER.

I'LL FIND MY WAY FROM HERE.

GUNNERY SERGEANT OCCAMPO...

...IT'S BEEN A **LONG** TIME.

TWELVE YEARS.

TECHNICALLY, MISS CARLYLE, YOU'RE NOT **AUTHORIZED** TO BE--

DON'T. DON'T **EVEN**.

I AM **ACTING** HEAD OF THIS FAMILY. UNTIL MY FATHER **RECOVERS** ENOUGH TO RESUME LEADERSHIP, I **AM** CARLYLE.

SO LET'S NOT PLAY **GAMES**.

I **DON'T** PLAY GAMES, MA'AM. I ACT ON **VERY** EXPLICIT ORDERS AS ISSUED BY YOUR **FATHER**.

STANDBY MODE

MY MISSION IS TO TRAIN, EDUCATE, AND **PROTECT** FOREVER CARLYLE.

YOU SENT GABRIEL MASON TO **KIDNAP** THAT LITTLE GIRL DOWN THERE.

MARK VIII OVERWATCH

STANDBY

YOU'RE **LUCKY** I HAVEN'T ALREADY THROWN YOUR ASS **OUT** OF HERE.

YOU **SHOT** GABRIEL MASON IN THE **HEAD**. TWICE.

HAVE YOU ASKED YOURSELF WHO LET YOU KNOW HE WAS **COMING?**

BUT IF YOU'D *RATHER* TALK ABOUT YOUR *MISSION*, I'M MORE THAN HAPPY TO DO *THAT*, TOO...

...BECAUSE YOU SEEM TO HAVE *FUCKED* IT INTO A COCKED *HAT*.

I WANT AN *EXPLANATION*.

EIGHT *DID* WHAT YOUR FAMILY HAS *MADE* HER AND *TRAINED* HER TO DO, MISS CARLYLE.

SHE MADE A *PLAN* AND *EXECUTED* IT.

...*TIMED* THE GUARD ROTATIONS, *CAPPED* THE SURVEILLANCE, *SPOOFED* THE SENSORS THROUGHOUT ALL OF ZONE KAPPA...

...JUST LIKE WE *TAUGHT* HER.

I WANT TO KNOW *WHO* TOLD HER SONJA BITTNER WAS HERE.

NO ONE TOLD HER. IT WAS BAD *TIMING*, THAT'S ALL. SHE JUST WANTED TO GO FOR A *WALK*.

YOU'RE TELLING ME IT WAS *COINCIDENCE?*

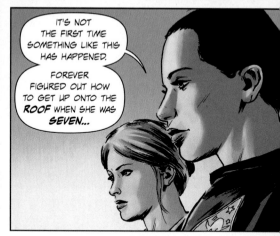

IT'S NOT THE FIRST TIME SOMETHING LIKE THIS HAS HAPPENED.

FOREVER FIGURED OUT HOW TO GET UP ONTO THE *ROOF* WHEN SHE WAS *SEVEN*...

...SHE USED TO SNEAK UP THERE AT NIGHT TO LOOK AT THE STARS.

IT TOOK US A *MONTH* TO FIGURE OUT WHY SHE WAS SUDDENLY SO *TIRED* ALL THE TIME.

IT'S WHERE EIGHT'S AT DEVELOPMENTALLY. SHE'S *CURIOUS*. SHE'S *LONELY*.

AND NOW SHE HAS A *FRIEND*.

YES, MA'AM.

SEPARATE THEM. **NO** FURTHER CONTACT.

FIRST THING I SAID TO SONJA WAS THAT SHE COULDN'T SAY **ANYTHING** ABOUT THIS TO **ANYONE**, ESPECIALLY NOT TO **EITHER** OF THEM.

SHE UNDERSTANDS, MISS CARLYLE. SHE **ADORES** YOUR SISTER, SHE'D **NEVER** DO ANYTHING TO HURT--

MARISOL.

UNTIL MISS BITTNER'S COMPLETED **CONDITIONING,** WE **CANNOT** TAKE THE RISK.

INFORM MISS BITTNER THAT SHE'S BEING **DEPLOYED...**

...IT'S TIME FOR HER TO TAKE THE FIGHT TO THE ENEMY.

HELLO, FOREVER.

Cheyenne Mountain, Colorado:
Carlyle Central Command (CENTCOM)
Family: Carlyle

CARLYLE CENTRAL COMMAND

GENERAL VALERI?

GIDEON SURVEILLANCE IS REPORTING HEAVY HOCK MOVEMENT OFF THE MISSISSIPPI BORDER...

Population [Serf]: 298

...MOSTLY IRREGULARS, HEADING NORTH. LIKELY IN RESPONSE TO OUR MOVING THE 682ND INTO THE REGION.

THEN HE'S TAKEN THE BAIT.

POSSIBLY. HIS OPTIONS ARE *LIMITED* UNTIL HE CAN MOVE TROOPS IN FOR A COUNTER-OFFENSIVE. LAST THING HE WANTS IS OUR COMBAT ENGINEERS TURNING HIS SAMS BACK ON HIM.

WHAT ABOUT THE MANUFACTURING CENTERS?

I'VE CHOPPED THE GROUND COMBAT ELEMENT FROM THE 13TH EXPEDITIONARY UNIT OVER TO THE AIR GROUP FOR INSERTION INTO *GREENSBORO* AND *ATLANTA*.

HAVANA IS STILL MAKING ME *NERVOUS*, THOUGH, EVEN WITH THE RELATIVELY *FRESH* INTEL.

WOULD A LAZARUS *REASSURE* YOU?

ABSOLUTELY, BUT MY UNDERSTANDING IS THAT YOUR SISTER--

NO, NOT MY SISTER...

...I'M SENDING YOU SONJA BITTNER.

SHE'S HAVING HER FINAL MEDICAL *NOW.*

YOU GIVE ME A LAZARUS, I CAN GIVE YOU THE HAVANA OBJECTIVE.

COMMENCE THE OPERATION AT YOUR DISCRETION, GENERAL.

KEEP ME POSTED.

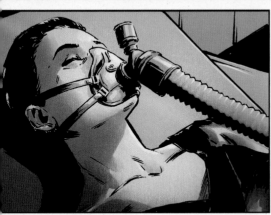

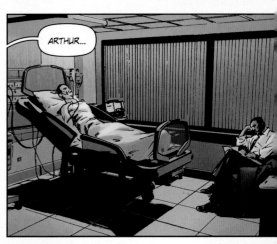

ARTHUR...

...HOW'S MY FATHER DOING?

HE'S BREATHING ON HIS OWN, NOW. SEEMS STABLE.

GENERAL VALERI WANTED TO TALK TO YOU.

WE JUST FINISHED.

I GAVE HIM THE GO-AHEAD.

IT'S *GOOD* STRATEGY, JO.

IMPAIRING HOCK'S ABILITY TO MANUFACTUR THE COMBAT DRUG HE'S FEEDING HIS TROOPS...

...MEANS WE'RE IMPAIRING HOCK HIMSELF, YES.

OF COURSE, HOCK *KNOWS* THAT AS WELL AS *WE* DO.

CAN YOU ARRANGE A MEETING WITH *ARMITAGE*, ARTHUR? COMS IF NEEDED, BUT IN-PERSON WOULD BE *BETTER*.

MIGHT TAKE SOME WORK, BUT IT'S CERTAINLY *DOABLE*...

...THOUGH IT'S MY **OPINION** THAT WE SHOULD BE FOCUSING ON OUR **OWN** PROBLEMS BEFORE WE CONSIDER OPENING **ANOTHER** FRONT IN **EUROPE**, JO.

HOCK **OPENED** IT BY **PROXY**, ARTHUR, AND ALL OF HIS **ALLIES** HAVE JOINED THE FIGHT.

IT'S THE FAMILIES THAT **HAVEN'T** MOVED YET THAT **CONCERN** ME...

...THE **WILD CARDS** WAITING FOR THEIR MOMENT TO **STRIKE**.

IT'S TIME WE **PUSHED** THEM INTO PLAY.

VASSALOVKA AND **LI** ESPECIALLY, THEY'RE--

DON'T ⇒kof⇐ WORRY ABOUT LI...

...I TOOK CARE OF THAT **YEARS** AGO ⇒kof kof⇐...

DADDY?

MALCOLM!

...IT'S **VASSALOVKA** THAT'S THE **VARIABLE**...

...THEY'LL **FEAST** ON THE FIRST ⇒kof⇐ WEAKNESS THEY **SEE**...

IT'S **OKAY**, DADDY. ARTHUR AND I HAVE **EVERYTHING** UNDER **CONTROL**.

WHERE'S MY LITTLE GIRL?

I'M RIGHT HERE, DADDY.

WHERE'S FOREVER?

Graubünden Canton, Switzerland — Davos

AHHHHH!!!!

CARLYLE BITCH!

I HAVE BEEN WAITING FOR THIS SINCE WE *MET*, FOREVER.

I SHOULD HAVE BEEN THE ONE TO *FIGHT* YOU AT THE *CONCLAVE*, INSTEAD OF THAT TRAITOR BITTNER *WHORE!*

I WOULD HAVE *BROKEN* YOUR BODY IN FRONT OF *EVERY* FAMILY!

I WOULD HAVE TAKEN YOUR *HEAD* WHILE YOUR FATHER *WEPT!*

MICHAEL LARK

CULL CHAPTER TWO

April, X+65
Graubünden Canton,
Switzerland – Davos

BLUE WOLF.

DAGGERS WILL STAND **DOWN**, PLEASE...

Family: Rausling
(occupied Bittner)

...THIS IS BETWEEN CAPTAIN **MUELLER** AND **MYSELF.**

DON'T GO **TOO** FAR...

...YOU'RE **NEXT** AFTER I FINISH WITH THIS BITTNER **BITCH.**

Ah, SONJA.

I AM GOING TO BRING LUKA RAUSLING YOUR **HEAD** ON A **PLATTER.**

COME AND **GET** IT.

Southern Sierra Nevadas:
Compound Sequoia

Family: Carlyle

Four weeks ago

SURGERY WENT **FLAWLESSLY,** EXACTLY LIKE I **SAID** IT WOULD...

Population [Family]: 4 [1 permanent]
Population [Serf]: 69

...THERE WAS NEVER AN ISSUE OF **REJECTION,** AND THE NEW LEG IS PERFORMING **PERFECTLY.**

SHE'S SUFFERING SOME LINGERING PAIN-- TO BE EXPECTED--AND HER **MOOD** HAS BEEN MORE **SUBDUED** THAN USUAL.

WHEN DO YOU START PHYSICAL **THERAPY?**

WE STARTED FOUR DAYS **AGO.**

JAMES AND MICHAEL ARE WITH HER AT P.T. **NOW.**

JAMES AND **WHO?**

DOCTOR BARRETT, I **KNOW** I TOLD YOU ABOUT HIM.

HE'S A FUCKING **GENIUS,** JO, MAYBE AS **SMART** AS MOM WAS.

AND BECAUSE OF **THAT** YOU'RE LETTING HIM TREAT FOREVER?

THIS YOUNG MAN IS **GIFTED.** I BROUGHT HIM IN TO HELP TREAT FATHER.

ONLY **TWENTY,** BUT...HE'S GOING TO BE **INVALUABLE** TO THE PROJECT.

WAIT, YOU BROUGHT HIM IN WITHOUT **CONSULTING** ME?

HOW MUCH DOES HE **KNOW?** DOES HE KNOW ABOUT **CONDITIONING?** ABOUT **EIGHT?**

I DON'T **NEED** YOUR PERMISSION TO--

LAZARUS PROGRAM ACCESS HAS TO BE **APPROVED** BY HEAD OF FAMILY!

WHICH WAS **STEPHEN!**

STEPHEN SAID **NOTHING** ABOUT THIS TO ME!

I WAS TRYING TO SAVE OUR FATHER'S **LIFE!**

YOU'RE ONLY **ACTING** H.O.F, ANYWAY, JOHANNA. NOW THAT FATHER'S **RECOVERING--**

I'M H.O.F. UNTIL FATHER SAYS **OTHERWISE,** AND HE HASN'T SAID IT **YET,** BETHANY.

HE **WILL.**

WELL, I'M GOING TO VISIT HIM **NEXT,** SO I'LL MAKE A POINT OF **ASKING** HIM FOR YOU.

BUT AT **THIS** MOMENT? **I'M** HEAD OF FAMILY, AND I WANT THIS GENIUS **GONE** UNTIL HE'S **VETTED** PROPERLY.

YOU'RE **SUCH A** BITCH.

RUNS IN THE **FAMILY.**

MAKE IT **HAPPEN,** BETH.

SLOW **DOWN.**

LET'S BRING THE **WEIGHT** DOWN--

NO...

...TURN IT **UP.**

PLEASE, JAMES. I CAN **DO** THIS.

FINE.

I CAN DO THIS.

I CAN DO THIS.

...I CAN--

BEAUTIFUL **BLADEWORK**, EVE! I'VE RARELY SEEN **BETTER**!

THANK YOU, FATHER.

SO PROUD OF YOU.

FOREVER NEEDS TO SHOWER AND CLEAN UP BEFORE MEETING WITH MS. KWAN.

AND IT MIGHT BE **WISE** TO GET YOU OUT OF THE **COLD** AS WELL, SIR.

THE COLD AND I ARE OLD FRIENDS, MARISOL. BUT WE **DON'T** WANT TO KEEP MS. KWAN WAITING.

WHAT IS IT **TODAY**?

CALCULUS.

I KINDA **HATE** IT.

YET YOU LOVE YOUR **LANGUAGE** CLASSES, AND MATH IS JUST--

--**ANOTHER** LANGUAGE, AND WHERE HAVE I HEARD **THAT** BEFORE?

HE USED TO SAY THAT TO **ME** ALL THE TIME.

HOW YOU DOING, LITTLE SISTER?

I'M DOING GOOD, THANK YOU.

WILL I SEE YOU LATER?

YOU BET.

I UNDERSTAND THE HAVANA **AND** ATLANTA OBJECTIVES HAVE BEEN **SECURED.**

MORRAY'S REINFORCING US IN CUBA AS WE SPEAK.

WHAT ABOUT GREENSBORO?

HOCK'S **FIGHTING** US EVERY INCH OF THE WAY. WE'RE PAYING IN A **LOT** OF BLOOD.

GENERAL VALERI IS ASKING FOR A **LAZARUS** TO ASSIST.

FOREVER'S IN **NO** CONDITION TO BE **REDEPLOYED.**

HE'S HOPING FOR **SONJA BITTNER.** WE USED HER IN **CUBA.**

HE'LL TAKE JOACQUIM OR WENING, IF HE CAN GET THEM.

EDGAR WON'T MOVE JOACQUIM AWAY FROM THE **FRONT** WITH **D'SOUZA.**

AND I DON'T SEE CARRAGHER SENDING MISS PERTIWI ACROSS THE **PACIFIC** WHEN HE'S **WORRYING** ABOUT **MINETTA.**

SO IT HAS TO BE SONJA.

GET SEVARA'S **BLESSING** FIRST. SONJA'S MOTHER IS FEELING **POWERLESS** RIGHT NOW. DON'T **RUB** IT IN.

SHE AND HER GIRLS ARE STAYING AT CENTER?

NO, IN VANCOUVER, WITH ARTHUR'S FAMILY.

GOOD. THAT'S GOOD.

AND YOU'VE BEEN CHECKING ON **YOUR** MOTHER?

YES, FATHER.

HOW DOES IT **FEEL?**

FATHER?

TO HAVE WHAT YOU **WANTED.**

YOU'RE **HEAD OF FAMILY.** THAT **IS** WHAT YOU'VE ALWAYS WANTED, **ISN'T** IT?

I WANTED TO **SUCCEED** YOU, **NOT** REPLACE YOU.

THE ONE **NECESSITATES** THE OTHER, JOHANNA.

YES. IT'S WHAT I **WANT.**

AND I'M **GOOD** AT IT.

YOU THINK SO, TOO. THAT'S **WHY** YOU HAVEN'T MADE ME STEP **DOWN** YET.

OR PERHAPS I'M TOO **WEAK** TO RESUME CONTROL.

IF THAT'S WHAT YOU WANT ME TO BELIEVE.

YOU'LL **CONTINUE** FOR THE TIME BEING.

WITH MY BLESSING.

THANK YOU.

YOU'RE THE ONE WHO HAD JONAH *KILLED*. I JUST WANTED HIM OUT OF MY *WAY*.

AND SPARED HIM RIGHT INTO A LIFE OF *TORTURE* AND *MISERY*.

JONAH'S CHOICES WERE HIS OWN.

YOU KNEW WHAT I WAS DOING AND YOU DIDN'T *STOP* ME. ALL PART OF YOUR *GRAND PLAN?*

PERHAPS.

SO I BETRAYED MY BROTHER, BUT YOU HAD YOUR *SON* MURDERED.

YOU WILL NOT *SHAME* ME WITH *MY* SINS, JOHANNA. I KNOW THEM *FAR* BETTER THAN YOU.

WE *NEED* FOREVER ON *OUR* SIDE, JOHANNA.

DO *WHATEVER* YOU MUST TO *KEEP* HER THERE.

San Francisco
Family: Carlyle

Population [Family]: 0
Population [Serf]: 361,890
Population [Waste]:
1,700,500 (estimated)

JUST A SEC!

HI, DAD.

MICHAEL!

Oh GOD, MICHAEL, IT'S SO GOOD TO SEE YOU....

--AT YOU, WE WERE **SO** WORRIED!

THE **BEST** WE COULD GET OUT OF THE SCHOOL WAS A MEETING WITH DEAN MUHR!

AND ALL **SHE** WOULD TELL US WAS THAT YOU WERE **HELPING** THE FAMILY WITH THE **WAR** EFFORT.

WHERE HAVE YOU BEEN?

I...I **HAVE** BEEN WORKING FOR THE FAMILY.

I'M NOT REALLY **ALLOWED** TO SAY ANYTHING **MORE.**

BOTH OF THEM.

YEAH.

WHAT?

CASEY'S THE **SAME.** NOT AS **MYSTERIOUS,** WE KNOW SHE WAS ON THE **FRONT.**

BUT SHE WON'T TELL US **WHERE.**

YOU'VE HEARD FROM CASEY? IS SHE ALL RIGHT?

SHE'S FINE.

AND SHE'S **REALLY** HAPPY TO SEE YOU.

nnn

FUCK.

FUCK **FUCK** FUCK **FUCK** FUCK.

DOCTOR MANN SAYS YOU TOOK A **FALL** DURING P.T.

NOW **THIS.**

JESUS CHRIST, FOREVER.

HAVEN'T YOU HURT YOURSELF **ENOUGH** TODAY?

THE *SILENT TREATMENT* IS GETTING *OLD*.

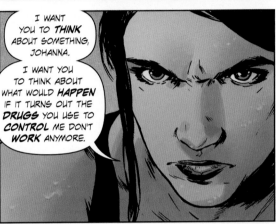

I WANT YOU TO *THINK* ABOUT SOMETHING, JOHANNA.

I WANT YOU TO THINK ABOUT WHAT WOULD *HAPPEN* IF IT TURNS OUT THE *DRUGS* YOU USE TO *CONTROL* ME DON'T *WORK* ANYMORE.

I *KNOW* WHAT YOU DID.

I KNOW *WHAT I AM*.

AND I WANT YOU TO GET OUT OF MY *WAY*. NOW.

THANK YOU.

Graubünden Canton,
Switzerland — Davos

SERGEANT PARK!

NICELY DONE, MA'AM.

YOU ARE KIND.

BURN HIS BODY.

YOU MAY INFORM GENERAL VALERI THAT WE HAVE **REMOVED** THE FIRST LAZARUS...

...AND THAT THE **ALLIED** INVASION OF EUROPE MAY **BEGIN**....

MICHAEL LARK

CULL

CHAPTER THREE

May, X+65
8.76 km north of Bastia, Corsica

Family: Rausling
Population [Family]: 2
Population [Serf- Active Duty
 Rausling Forces]: 1,200 (est.)

Population [Waste]: 190,500 (est.)

BASILISK_TRANSMISSION_0509889/7_AA_
SEC: BLACK_BLACK_BLACK
SENDER: ADM. SANGER, R._CARSEC/INT_
SUBJ: OPERATION_CANDLELIGHT
STAND-BY TO RECEIVE_

MESSAGE BEGINS

GIDEON_ANALYTIC REPORT:
%91.73 PROBABLE TARGET DESIGNATED
   PEREGRINE WILL ATTEMPT EXFIL
   VIA BASTIA CORSICA _|_|_
%67.93 PROBABLE D'SOUZA ASSETS
   EN ROUTE TO AID EXTRACTION_|_|_
DAGGER TEAM ALPHA DIRECTED TO
   ELIMINATE TARGET PEREGRINE_|_|_

SAY AGAIN:
DAGGER TEAM ALPHA DIRECTED
   ELIMINATE TARGET PEREGRINE_|_|_
ADDITIONAL ALLIED ASSET ASSIGNED
   THIS OPERATION_|_|_
ACTION AUTHORIZED BY H_O_F_
   THIS DATE_|_|_
ADDITIONAL FROM H_O_F
   TO DAGGER ALPHA:

''KILL THE RAUSLING
   SON OF A BITCH''_|_|_

MESSAGE ENDS

SUPPORT
VEHICLES **OUT.**

COWBOY,
BLUE WOLF.

PEREGRINE IS
OPEN, REPEAT,
PEREGRINE IS
OPEN...

...HE'S
ALL **YOURS.**

NNYAAAA!!

AHH!

...HELP...

...SOMEONE, PLEASE...

...PLEASE... PLEASE NO...

...ANYTHING, I'LL...I'LL GIVE YOU **ANYTHING**--

--I DON'T WANT TO **DIE** I--

--PLEASE....

BLUE WOLF, COWBOY. VEHICLE NEUTRALIZED.

PEREGRINE ON TRACK.

CONFIRMED. WE'RE EN ROUTE.

THAT WON'T BE **NECESSARY**, MY FRIEND...

...THIS WILL NOT TAKE VERY **LONG**....

IT'S YOUR MOVE.

FOREVER? YOUR MOVE?

I KNOW.

GO AHEAD.

I KNOW.

I KNOW WHAT I *AM*, FATHER.

IF I CAN EVEN *CALL* YOU THAT.

OF COURSE YOU CAN CALL ME THAT.

HOW? YOU... YOU HAD ME *MADE*. IN A *LAB*. TO BE A *WEAPON*, TO BE *YOUR* WEAPON.

YOU *LIED* TO ME, AND YOU--YOU USE *DRUGS*...

...TO MAKE ME *BELIEVE* YOU, ALL YOUR *LIES*--

FOREVER.

--DON'T *TOUCH* ME--

--TO KEEP ME *LOYAL*, TO MAKE ME *LOVE* YOU AND BETH AND STEPHEN AND JOHANNA...

...CALLING ME YOUR *DAUGHTER*, TELLING ME THIS IS MY *FAMILY*, THAT I'M *CARLYLE*...

...AND IT'S JUST A *LIE* AND I SHOULD'VE *KNOWN* AND I THINK MAYBE I *DID* BUT I DIDN'T WANT IT TO BE *TRUE*....

BUT IT *IS*.

IT'S ALL BEEN A *LIE*.

ALL I CAN SAY IS THIS.

FEW THINGS ARE AS **SIMPLE** AS WE IMAGINE THEM TO BE, FOREVER.

IF YOUR MOTHER HAD **CARRIED** YOU NINE MONTHS, OR IF WE HAD **ADOPTED** YOU INSTEAD OF **ENGINEERING** YOU, YOU WOULD **STILL** BE MY DAUGHTER...

...AND YOU WOULD **STILL** BE THE DAUGHTER I **WANTED.**

GOOD NIGHT, FOREVER.

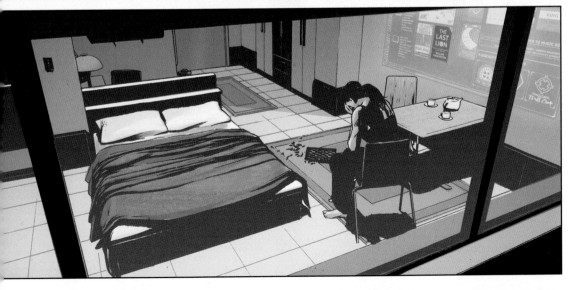

San Francisco
Family: Carlyle

Population [Family]: 0
Population [Serf]: 361,890
Population [Waste]: 1,700,500 (estimated)

--MY ARM, MIKE, CAREFUL--

CASEY--

--MIKE oh oh oh MICHAEL *MICHAEL*!!!

--*CASEY*!!!

...JUST... THAT WAS...

Unf

...I *NEEDED* THAT.

Mmmf.

da-ding

da-ding

WE WERE TOO NOISY.

NOT NEARLY NOISY ENOUGH.

da-ding

WHOEVER THE FUCK IT IS, I'M FUCKING TELLING THEM TO GO THE FUCK *AWAY*.

THAT WAS A LOT OF "FUCK."

MORE WHERE THAT CAME FROM, SCIENCE-BOY.

CAN I HELP YOU?

THIS IS THE BARRETT RESIDENCE?

IT IS, BUT JOE AND BOBBIE ARE *OUT* RIGHT NOW...

...YOU'LL HAVE TO COME BACK--

DELIVERY FOR CORPORAL SOLOMON, CASEY J.

YOUR CHIP IS *VERIFIED*.

WHAT?

WAIT, *WHAT?*

HAVE A NICE DAY.

CASEY?

WHO WAS IT?

SOLOMON, CASEY J. CORPORAL 6151002/041564

HOLY SHIT.

WHAT'S UP?

HOLY SHIT!

I'VE BEEN ORDERED TO REPORT FOR DAGGER SELECTION....

--NEED TO GET IN *FRONT* OF THIS, AND WE NEED TO DO IT *NOW!*

SETTLE *DOWN,* BETHANY.

IF I'M *CONCERNED,* FATHER, IT'S *ONLY* BECAUSE WE'VE BEEN HERE *BEFORE.*

WE'VE GOT TO *UP* HER MEDS OR WE'RE GOING TO LOSE *ALL* CONTROL OVER FOREVER.

THAT HASN'T WORKED VERY WELL IN THE PAST.

WE'VE *ADJUSTED* THE REGIMEN SINCE THEN, WE HAVE A *MUCH* BETTER GRASP OF THE DRUG INTERACTIONS.

I KNOW WHAT YOU'RE *THINKING,* JAMES, BUT IT'LL BE *DIFFERENT* THIS TIME.

OR IT WILL BE *HISTORY* REPEATING ITSELF.

IT *WILL* BE *DIFFERENT* THIS TIME, FATHER.

WE LEARNED A LOT. AND THERE'S REALLY NO *OTHER* CHOICE.

WE COULD TELL HER THE **TRUTH.**

ARE YOU OUT OF YOUR **FUCKING** MIND?

WE'LL LOSE **ALL** CONTROL OVER HER!

THE **PSYCHOLOGICAL** DAMAGE...JOHANNA, THERE'S NO WAY TO KNOW HOW SHE'LL **REACT--**

WHY **NOT?** SHE'S **HALFWAY** THERE ALREADY.

I THINK WE NEED TO **SERIOUSLY** CONSIDER IT.

IF WE WEREN'T AT WAR, IT **MIGHT** BE WORTH PURSUING.

BUT I'M INCLINED TO AGREE WITH YOUR SISTER AND JAMES. IT'S **VERY** RISKY.

I THINK THAT'S A **MISTAKE.**

GO AHEAD AND **ADJUST** HER REGIME.

WE'LL SEE IF THAT DOESN'T **MODIFY** HER BEHAVIOR.

AT ONCE, FATHER.

MISS CARLYLE!

MISS!

GOOD EVENING.

YOU CAN RELAX, GUYS. I JUST CAME IN TO SAY HELLO.

AS YOU WERE.

YES, MISS.

ALL QUIET ON THE WESTERN FRONT?

I'M SORRY, MISS?

OLD JOKE, NEVER MIND...

...JUST MAKING SURE EVERYONE'S **SAFE** AND **SNUG** IN THEIR BEDS...

ding-ding-ding

TO: CARLYLE_FOREVER
FROM: %2FUNKNOWN%3AERROR

HE IS NOT
YOUR FATHER.

THIS IS NOT
YOUR FAMILY.

GO AWAY.

COME
WITH ME. QUICKLY.

WHY WOULD
I DO **ANYTHING**
YOU ASK, JO?

BECAUSE
I'M GOING TO
TELL YOU THE
TRUTH.

COME ON.

...MIDDLE OF A *WAR* AND YOU DECIDED TO HAVE A *CRISIS* OF *FAITH.*

WHERE ARE WE *GOING?*

YOU'LL SEE.

I HEARD ABOUT WHAT YOU SAID TO *DAD.* I IMAGINE A *LOT* OF IT EXTENDS TO ME. HOW WE'VE *LIED* TO YOU.

YOU'VE *USED* ME. *ALL* OF YOU...

...AND *YOU* MOST OF *ALL.*

OF *COURSE* WE'VE *USED* YOU! YOU'RE OUR FAMILY'S *LAZARUS!*

WHAT WERE WE SUPPOSED TO *DO,* TEACH YOU TO MAKE *BALLOON* ANIMALS AND HOST A FUCKING KID'S SHOW ON THE POST?

YOU'RE NOT JUST *OUR* LAZARUS, YOU'RE *THE* LAZARUS!

YOU'RE THE ONE *EVERY* OTHER FAMILY MEASURES *AGAINST,* FOR FUCK'S SAKE!

YOU'RE THE *HEART* OF CARLYLE, FOREVER. HEARTS GET BROKEN.

BUT THEY *MEND.*

H.O.F. ACCESS, GRANTED.

WHAT IS THIS?

⚠ WARNING

☣ Biohazard. Authorized personnel only.

7.90 km north of Bastia, Corsica

huff
huff huff

huff--
--unnhh

huff
huff huff

huff
huff hu--

--ff--

GOOD EVENING, LUKA.

huff SONJA *huff*

NO, **DON'T** GET UP.

IT ISN'T AS IF THERE'S [S]OMEPLACE FOR [Y]OU TO **GO,** IS THERE?

huff huff huff JOACQUIM *huff* MORRAY *huff*

GOOD EVENING, HERR RAUSLING.

YOU BROUGHT THIS UPON YOURSELF, LUKA.

YOU [H]AVE NOWHERE [L]EFT TO RUN. [Y]OU HAVE NO **ALLIES** TO **RELY** UPON.

THERE'S ONLY **YOU,** THE **LAST** BRANCH OF A **DEAD** FAMILY.

SO TOO IS **YOURS!** BITTNER IS **DEAD!**

AND **MORRAY** WILL **FOLLOW!**

CARLYLE HAS NO **ALLIES,** ONLY THOSE HE **USES** AND--

CULL CHAPTER FOUR

May, X+65

"...CONTINUING THEIR **RAPID** AND **RELENTLESS** RECOVERY OF FAMILY BITTNER TERRITORY THROUGHOUT WESTERN EUROPE, NOW **LIBERATED** IN THE WAKE OF THE RAUSLING FAMILY'S **COLLAPSE**...

"...WITH COMBAT OPERATIONS PRIMARILY **LIMITED** TO THE SUPPORT OF ONGOING HUMANITARIAN **RELIEF** EFFORTS.

"FOR REASONS OF **OPERATIONAL SECURITY**, I AM, OF COURSE, NOT PERMITTED TO DISCLOSE OUR **EXACT** LOCATION.

"WHAT I **CAN** SAY IS THAT I'VE WITNESSED FIRSTHAND THE **COOPERATION** AMONGST CARLYLE ALLIES, INCLUDING ELEMENTS FROM **MORRAY**...

"...AS WELL AS **ARMITAGE**, ALL **UNITED** IN THEIR EFFORTS TO DEFEAT WHAT REMAINS OF THE RAUSLING RESISTANCE.

"FOR NOW, THE FIGHTING HAS **STOPPED**...

...I'M SERÉ COOPER, AND YOU'VE BEEN
WATCHING A LIT LIVESTREAM, FROM DEEP
WITHIN LIBERATED RAUSLING TERRITORY...

...AND *CUT*, JUST...

...THAT WAS *CRAP.*

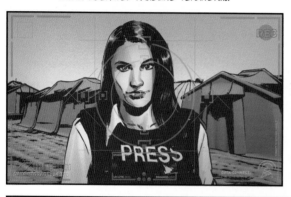

54 km east of Frankfurt
an der Oder, Germany
Family: ~~Rausling~~ Bittner

Population [Family]: 0̶ 1

Population [Serf- Active Duty
Rausling Forces]: 5,000 (est)

Population [Serf - Active Duty
Coalition Forces]: 10,250 (est)

IT WASN'T *THAT* BAD.

I LOVE
YOU, LUIS, BUT
TRUST ME.
CRAP.

EVEN
THE *VISUAL*
WAS CRAP..

...WE NEED
SOMETHING WITH
MORE *MEAT...*

...FOLLOW ME.

Oh, NO, NO, THIS IS **NOT A GOOD** IDEA, CEE.

IT'S A **GREAT** IDEA. SONJA BITTNER, FIRST EVER BATTLEFIELD **INTERVIEW** WITH A **LAZARUS**...

...THAT'S A **THIRD** SHONA AWARD, RIGHT THERE.

FOR YOU.

AND YOUR **FIRST.**

IF BROADCAST OVERSIGHT DOESN'T **SPIKE** IT AND **FIRE** US, LIEUTENANT MAYES IS GONNA BE BACK **ANY** MINUTE--

WHICH IS WHY WE'VE GOT TO MOVE **FAST.**

THEY WON'T **FIRE** US, LUIS.

MEANING THEY WON'T FIRE **YOU.**

US. C'MON, SAY IT **WITH** ME. SHONA AWARD WINNER.

C'MON.

CEE...

SHONA. AWARD...

...WINNER.

WE'RE GOING TO BE SENT **DOWN,** YOU KNOW THAT, RIGHT?

THINK SHE WENT **THAT** WAY....

...THE **BENEFIT** THAT DEAR DEPARTED LUKA ALREADY HAD HIS ARTILLERY **PRE-SIGHTED** ALONG THE POTENTIAL **ROUTES.**

WITH GOOD REASON, THOMAS. VASSALOVKA HAS **NEVER** BEEN A FAMILY TO TAKE **LIGHTLY.**

SO **TWO** CHOICES, FIGURE THE SCARY BEAR IS COMING TO VISIT GRANDMA VIA RED ROUTE **ONE**...

...OR RED ROUTE **TWO,** YES.

OR **BOTH.**

AND TO THINK SHE WAS SO **SWEET** AND **INNOCENT** AT THE CONCLAVE ALL THOSE MONTHS **AGO.**

SHE'S ALL GROWN **UP,** JOACQUIM.

I DO NOT THINK SONJA WAS EVER SO SWEET OR INNOCENT AS YOU **IMAGINE,** THOMAS.

A MAN CAN DREAM.

WE NEED BETTER **RECON.**

AGREED.

I CAN SPEAK TO MAJOR DONALD...

...PLAN AN INSERTION WITH DAGGER TEAM BRAVO--

--MAY WE **HELP** YOU?

YES.

YES, YOU **CAN.**

Population [Family]: 5 [2 permanent]
Population [Serf]: 68

da-deet
da-deet

FOREVER? JUST WANTED TO SAY GOOD **NIGHT**...

MARISOL? JAMES.

HAVE YOU SEEN FOREVER?

THIS... ...THIS... IS *ME*...

...*ALL* OF THESE--THESE *THINGS*...

...HOW...HOW *MANY* OF ME *ARE* THERE?

THESE *AREN'T* YOU.

THESE ARE JUST...*SPARE* PARTS...

...THE PIECES JAMES AND BETHANY *GROW* TO KEEP YOU *GOING.*

LOSE AN *ARM*, LOSE A *LEG*, LOSE A *LUNG*, DOESN'T *MATTER*.

WHAT YOU CAN'T *HEAL* YOURSELF, THEY'LL REPLACE IT *FOR* YOU.

I'M A *MONSTER*. THAT'S WHAT I *AM*, I'M A *MONSTER* AND--

NO.

YOU'RE *NOT* THE MONSTER HERE.

I'M NOT EVEN--I'M A *CLONE*, JUST A *COPY*--

IT DOESN'T *WORK* LIKE THAT.

THEN HOW THE FUCK *DOES* IT WORK?

YOU WERE *MADE*, YOU *KNOW* THAT. GROWN IN THE *LAB*.

BUT THERE ARE *OTHERS*, THERE HAVE BEEN *OTHERS*.

YES.

HOW MANY?

FOREVER--

HOW *MANY,* JOHANNA?

YOU'RE THE *SEVENTH.*

THE *FIRST* ONE WHERE EVERYTHING WORKED AS INTENDED. I TOLD YOU, YOU'RE NOT *A LAZARUS...*

...YOU'RE *THE* LAZARUS.

THERE'S *NEVER* BEEN ANYONE LIKE YOU.

NO OTHER FAMILY HAS COME *CLOSE.*

WHAT HAPPENED TO THEM? TO THE *OTHERS?*

I DON'T KNOW. DEAD. THE FIRST COUPLE WERE PURE *EXPERIMENTS,* PROOF-OF-CONCEPT. THE OTHERS...

...THE SCIENCE HAS NEVER BEEN *MY FORTÉ.* THINGS WENT *WRONG* WITH THE GENETICS OR THE MEDICATIONS OR... I DON'T KNOW.

IT TOOK A *LONG* TIME BEFORE THEY GOT IT *PERFECT,* BEFORE THEY MADE *YOU.*

SO I'M THE *ONLY* ONE?

JO?

AM I THE *ONLY* FOREVER CARLYLE?

THEY'RE TRAINING A **NEW** ONE, THE WAY **YOU** WERE TRAINED.

A **REPLACEMENT**, IN CASE SOMETHING **HAPPENS** TO YOU.

SHE'S NOT **READY** YET.

WHAT DOES **THAT** MEAN?

SHE'S **ELEVEN**.

DOES SHE **KNOW?**

THAT YOU EXIST? OF COURSE **NOT**.

YOU'RE NOT SUPPOSED TO KNOW, YOU WERE **NEVER** SUPPOSED TO KNOW **ANY** OF THIS.

FATHER WILL **KILL** ME--HE **WILL** KILL ME, DO YOU UNDERSTAND?--IF HE **EVER** FINDS OUT I BROUGHT YOU **HERE**, THAT I TOLD YOU THIS.

HE'S **THAT** AFRAID OF ME KNOWING THE TRUTH?

NOT **JUST** HIM.

JAMES?

I'VE CHECKED *EVERYWHERE.*

SHE'S NOT IN HER QUARTERS, SHE'S NOT IN ANY OF THE *GYMS,* SHE'S NOT ON THE *RANGE....*

DID YOU CHECK THE ROOF?

SHE USED TO GO UP--

I REMEMBER. SHE'S NOT ON THE *ROOF,* MARISOL.

I'M NOT SURE I FOLLOW THE *CONCERN.* ZONE KAPPA'S BEEN IN *LOCKDOWN* SINCE EIGHT WENT WALKABOUT--

SHE KNOWS MALCOLM'S BEEN *LYING* TO HER.

WE'VE BEEN TRYING TO RE-*ASSERT* CONDITIONING, BUT IT HASN'T HAD TIME TO *TAKE* YET AND SHE'S BEEN *FIGHTING* IT.

IT'S HAPPENING *AGAIN,* MARISOL.

WHEN WAS THE LAST TIME ANYONE SAW HER?

THIS MORNING, SHE DID P.T., PUT IN SOME RANGE TIME, THEN WENT BACK TO HER ROOM.

IF SHE'S DECIDED TO *LEAVE* AND DIDN'T WANT US TO KNOW...

Oh, EASILY. OVER TWELVE HOURS? SHE COULD BE *OUT* OF FAMILY TERRITORY BY NOW AND HALFWAY TO AUSTRALIA.

DID YOU RUN *TELEMETRY?*

WE *DISABLED* IT WHEN WE *OPERATED* ON HER, WE HADN'T BROUGHT IT BACK *ONLINE* YET, THERE HADN'T BEEN A *NEED...*

YOU FUCKING *IDIOTS.*

WE NEED TO INFORM MALCOLM AND JOHANNA, WE--

NOT *YET.* LET ME DO A *HARD* SEARCH BEFORE WE ASSUME THE *WORST.*

YOU SHOULD'VE *TOLD* HER, JAMES.

ALL OF YOU, YOU SHOULD'VE TOLD HER *YEARS* AGO.

I WANT TO **MEET** HER.

TIME REMAINING:

THE **YOUNGER** ME, I WANT TO MEET HER.

YOU WANT ME TO **TRUST** YOU. THAT'S **HOW** YOU DO IT.

YOU'RE **NOT** THINKING AND WE'RE RUNNING OUT OF **TIME**.

WE'VE GOT FIVE AND A HALF MINUTES TO GET OUT OF HERE BEFORE THE ALARMS COME BACK ONLINE.

I THINK THAT'S MORE **YOUR** PROBLEM THAN MINE.

YOU'RE **OUT** OF **CONDITIONING**. SHE'S **DEEP** IN IT.

THINK ABOUT WHAT YOU'RE ASKING, AND THEN THINK ABOUT HOW **YOU** WERE AT THAT AGE.

IF SHE'S ME, SHE CAN **HANDLE** IT.

BUT SHE'S **NOT** YOU. SHE'S **HER**, SAME **TEMPLATE**, DIFFERENT **STRUCTURE** BUILT ON IT.

EVERYTHING THEY **DID**, EVERYTHING DADDY **SAID** TO YOU, **ALL** THE MEDICATIONS, **EVERY** LIE, IT'S FOR **ONE** REASON AND ONE REASON **ONLY**.

TO **CONTROL** YOU. AND THEY'VE GOTTEN EVEN **BETTER** AT IT WITH **HER**.

YOU WANT TO CONTROL ME, **TOO**. THIS IS JUST ANOTHER WAY TO **DO** IT.

NO--

DON'T **LIE** TO ME, JO. NOT **ANYMORE**. NOT **HERE**.

FOREVER, WE'RE **HERE** BECAUSE I **DON'T** WANT TO **LIE** TO YOU ANYMORE.

WE'RE HERE BECAUSE SOMEONE HAS TO TELL YOU THE **TRUTH**, AND EVERYONE UPSTAIRS IS TOO FUCKING SCARED TO **DO** IT.

BECAUSE THEY'LL LOSE CONTROL.

YES.

SO YOU SHOW ME THIS, SO YOU **GAIN** CONTROL.

I DON'T WANT TO--

I SAID, **DON'T** LIE--

I THOUGHT I **DID!**

I THOUGHT I **HAD** TO! **DADDY** CONTROLLED YOU, I NEEDED TO GET YOU **FROM** HIM OR GET YOU **GONE!**

BUT I WAS **WRONG...**

...I WAS WRONG ABOUT A **LOT** OF THINGS.

THREE MINUTES.

TIME REMAINING: 02:59:17

>>>ALERT<<<

WHAT **DO** YOU WANT?

IT DOESN'T MATTER. WE'RE OUT OF **TIME.** WHEN FATHER FINDS OUT, I'M DEAD, AND YOU...

...BETHANY WILL UP YOUR **CONDITIONING** SO MUCH YOU WON'T BE ABLE TO DO ANYTHING BUT **OBEY.**

THEY CAN **DO** THAT?

THEY WON'T BE **HAPPY** ABOUT IT, IT'LL DESTROY YOUR PERSONALITY, IT'LL QUOTE IMPAIR-YOUR-COGNITIVE-ABILITIES-END QUOTE.

BUT THEY'LL **DO** IT, AT LEAST UNTIL YOUR **REPLACEMENT** IS READY.

TELL ME WHAT YOU **WANT**, JO.

I WANT YOU ON MY **SIDE.**

I WANT YOU ON MY SIDE BECAUSE THAT'S WHERE **YOU** WANT TO BE.

TO DO **WHAT?**

TO **CHANGE** THE **WORLD.**

BECAUSE I DON'T KNOW IF YOU'VE **NOTICED,** BUT THE WORLD IS PRETTY FUCKING **BROKEN** RIGHT NOW.

AND DADDY'S WAY SURE AS HELL ISN'T MAKING IT **BETTER.**

THEY'RE GIVING ME THE DRUGS *AGAIN*, JO. I'VE BEEN *CHEATING* ON THEM, BUT I CAN'T CUT THEM OUT ENTIRELY.

IF I *DON'T* TAKE THEM I GET *SICK*, I DON'T *WORK* RIGHT, AND IF I *DO...*

I KNOW.

YOU HAVE TO FIGURE OUT HOW TO *CHANGE* MY MEDICATION WITHOUT THEM *KNOWING.*

SO I CAN *DO* WHAT I NEED TO DO, SO THAT I CAN BE *ME*, SO I CAN THINK FOR *MYSELF.*

HOW MUCH TIME DO WE HAVE?

FIFTY-THREE SECONDS.

CAN YOU DO IT? *WILL* YOU DO THAT FOR ME?

YES.

BUT IT'S *TOO* LATE, WE'RE--

I GOT *BUSTED* FOR GOING UP ON THE *ROOF* WHEN I WAS LITTLE.

THEY DIDN'T REALIZE I'D PRETTY MUCH *MAPPED* THE ENTIRE FACILITY, EVERYWHERE I COULD *REACH.*

HEY!

NEVER COULD MAKE IT DOWN *HERE...*

...NOW I KNOW *WHY....*

NOTHING.

WE HAVE TO *TELL* THEM.

YES.

I LOVE HER.

I KNOW, JAMES.

I DO, TOO....

SECURICAM_FEEDCYCLE: RUNNING

CAMERA BANK: L-4A
2X
BACKUP TO STACK G

--NEEDED *ANOTHER* LAYER IF WE WERE GOING TO BE *OUT* FOR THAT LONG.

IT'S NOT *THAT* COLD.

NOT TO *YOU*, MAYBE. ME, I'M FREEZING MY *TITS* OFF.

ZONE ALP

DOCTOR MANN, SERGEANT OCCAMPO. WHAT'RE YOU TWO STILL DOING *UP*?

JUST MAKING THE ROUNDS.

WHERE'VE *YOU* TWO BEEN?

ZONE A

MY SISTER AND I HAD SOME... THINGS TO TALK ABOUT.

AND SHE *INSISTED* WE TALK ABOUT THEM *OUTSIDE.*

IN THE *COLD.*

I'M HEADING TO *BED.*

I'M GLAD WE TALKED, JO.

I AM, *TOO.* SLEEP *WELL.*

ZONE ALPHA

ZONE ALPHA

EVERYTHING... EVERYTHING ALL RIGHT, MISS CARLYLE?

I THINK SO, JAMES.

I THINK SO.

3.7 km west of Rzepin, Poland
Family: Rausling Disputed

...LIKE WE *AGREED*, RIGHT?

YOU STAY *BACK*, YOU DO WHAT *I* SAY, YOU GET YOUR FOOTAGE TO RUN WITH THE *INTERVIEW*...

...AND THEN I GET TO TAKE YOU TO *DINNER* WHEN WE'RE BACK IN LONDON.

AGREED, BUT I'M WARNING YOU, I'M *NOT* CHEAP, SIR THOMAS.

MISS COOPER, I WOULDN'T WANT TO TAKE YOU OUT TO DINNER IF YOU *WERE*.

WE'LL DO A *BREACH* ON THE FARMHOUSE, GIVE YOU SOMETHING NICE FOR THE CAMERA. I'LL LET YOU KNOW WHEN YOU CAN COME *IN*.

IS IT *SAFE*?

WE SENT AN *ADVANCE* TEAM IN AN HOUR AGO TO DO A *RECCE*.

NO DANGER, JUST A FAMILY OF *FIVE* WHO'LL BE *MOR* THAN HAPPY TO *ENTHUSIASTICALLY* WELCOME LIBERATION FROM RAUSLING'S *TYRANNY*.

YOU'RE *SURE*?

IF THEY WANT THE NEW *TRUCK* THEY WERE PROMISED, THEY DAMN WELL *BETTER*.

YOU'RE GETTING THIS? I'M **RECORDING.**

I WISH WE COULD DO THIS **LIVE.** IT'S LIKE YOU'RE **TRYING** TO GET US FIRED, I SWEAR TO GOD.

I'LL SQUARE IT WITH LIEUTENANT MAYES. YEAH? YOU GONNA LET HIM TAKE YOU OUT TO DINNER, TOO? FUCK YOU, LUIS.

COME ON. SIR THOMAS **SAID**-- I KNOW WHAT HE SAID, COME **ON.**

CLEAR **OUT,** EVERYONE--

--CLEAR **OUT**-- Oh MY GOD.

--FALL **BACK** BLOODY **NOW,** HE COULD **STILL** BE **HERE!** AND TURN THAT FUCKING CAMERA **OFF!**

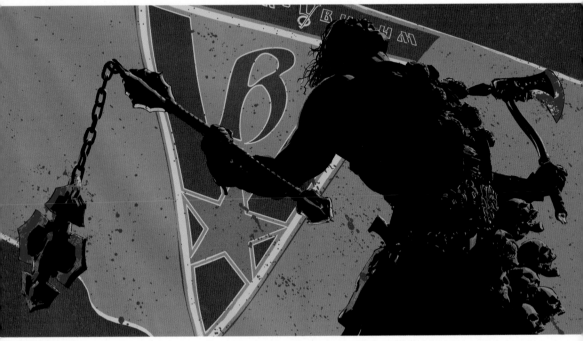

MICHAEL LARK

CULL CHAPTER FIVE

"WHAT I'M SAYING COMES DOWN TO **THIS**, COMMANDER..."

"...DON'T TRUST **ANYTHING** OR **ANYONE** ONCE YOU'VE GOT YOUR **BOOTS** ON THE **GROUND**...."

WHERE?

WE THINK THE CHURCH.

AREA IS **SECURE?**

AS SECURE AS WE CAN MAKE IT.

BLUE WOLF AND DAGGER ALPHA HAVE **WITHDRAWN** TO A SAFE **PERIMETER.**

IT IS GOOD TO SEE YOU AGAIN, FOREVER.

WOULD BE **BETTER** UNDER BETTER **CIRCUMSTANCES.**

Seven days ago

Golden Gate Park, San Francisco
Family: Carlyle

Population [Family]: 0
Population [Serf]: 361,890
Population [Waste]:
1,700,500 (estimated)

DOCTOR BARRETT. I DON'T BELIEVE WE'VE BEEN PROPERLY **INTRODUCED**.

I'M JOHANNA CARLYLE.

YES.

YES, YOU ARE.

YOU'RE **SCARED** OF ME.

I'D BE A FOOL **NOT** TO BE.

NICE TO KNOW YOU'RE NOT A **FOOL**.

I NEED YOUR **HELP**, DOCTOR BARRETT.

YOU NEED **MY** HELP?

WELL, **NOT** ME, NO...

...MY **SISTER**, ACTUALLY....

Southern Sierra Nevadas:
Compound Sequoia
Family: Carlyle

Population [Family]:
4 [2 permanent]

...NONAGINTA SEPTEM...NONAGINTA ET OCTO...

Population [Serf]: 68

hff

GOOD, *GOOD!* USE YOUR *HIPS!*

TIME FOR YOUR REGIMEN...

...FOREVER, AND IF WE CAN *SPARE* THE ATTITUDE *THIS* TIME?

HOLD YOUR **HORSES,** STILL NEED TO DO YOUR **INJECTION.**

JA-AMES.

I KNOW, I KNOW...

IT'S FOR YOUR **OWN** GOOD, FOREVER.

TRY TO **REMEMBER** THAT.

YES, BETH.

"WHERE ARE WE WITH THE CHANGE IN THE REGIMEN?"

EIGHT'S RESPONDING--

WAIT A MOMENT, WHERE'S JO?

I BELIEVE SHE'S AT CENTER.

I JUST THOUGHT AS **ACTING** HEAD OF FAMILY SHE MIGHT WANT TO BE **HERE**, THAT'S **ALL**, FATHER.

THERE **IS** A WAR ON, BETHANY. NOW, WHERE ARE WE?

AS I WAS SAYING, EIGHT IS RESPONDING **VERY** WELL TO THE NEW REGIMEN. NO CONTRAINDICATIONS, NO COMPLICATIONS AT **ALL**.

OUR INTENTION IS TO ACTIVATE THE NEXT SET OF **AUGMENTS** BY THE END OF JUNE.

MAKE CERTAIN MARISOL IS FULLY **BRIEFED**, SHE'LL NEED TO ACCOUNT FOR THE NEW ABILITY SUITE IN EIGHT'S **TRAINING**.

WHAT ABOUT FOREVER?

SHE STARTED THE **NEW** COURSE A COUPLE DAYS AGO.

IT'LL BE ANOTHER WEEK BEFORE IT'S COMPLETED. WE'LL KNOW **MORE** THEN.

CHECK HER **BLOODWORK**.

SHE'S **MORE** THAN CAPABLE OF **TRICKING** US INTO BELIEVING SHE'S DOING WHAT WE'VE ASKED.

I'M **NOT** CERTAIN WE NEED TO BE OVERLY **CONCERNED**.

JO HAD A HEART-TO-HEART WITH FOREVER LAST WEEK, AND EVE'S ATTITUDE-- WHILE NOT WHAT IT **WAS**--SEEMS TO HAVE **IMPROVED**.

HAS IT, INDEED?

I DON'T UNDERSTAND.

YES, YOU **DO.**

IF YOU'RE AS **SMART** AS MY SISTER THINKS YOU ARE-- AND I CHECKED UP ON YOU, AND YOU **ARE**--YOU **ABSOLUTELY** DO.

SOME OF THE MEDICATIONS DOCTOR MANN HAD ME GIVING MISS BITTNER...AT FIRST I THOUGHT I JUST DIDN'T **UNDERSTAND** THE GENE THERAPY.

BUT YOU DON'T NEED **MOOD-ALTERING** DRUGS TO INFLUENCE INDUCTION TRIGGERS.

IT JUST... WASN'T MY PLACE TO **ASK.**

IT'S ALL RIGHT, MICHAEL. YOU CAN **SAY** IT.

IT'S HOW YOU **CONTROL** THEM.

TO INFLUENCE HOW THEY **FEEL** ABOUT YOU, HOW THEY CAN **THINK.**

YES, WE DO.

IT'S WRONG.

THEY'RE NOT *BULLETS*, MICHAEL, THEY'RE *PEOPLE*.

VERY *DANGEROUS* PEOPLE IF THEY'RE NOT KEPT IN *CHECK*.

OR WOULD YOU RATHER A WORLD *RULED* BY LAZARI?

YOU KNOW THAT MY SISTER--THAT FOREVER--IS ON THE *SAME* MEDICATIONS.

SEEMED SELF-EVIDENT.

AS I UNDERSTAND IT, THE DRUGS DO *TWO* THINGS. THEY MAINTAIN THEIR *ABILITIES*, PRIMARILY *REGENERATIVE*, AND THEY ENFORCE THEIR *LOYALTY*.

HERE'S MY *QUESTION*:

CAN THEY BE *SEPARATED* WITHOUT IMPAIRING THOSE *ABILITIES?*

Oh, *ABSOLUTELY*. THE ONE HAS *NO* BEARING ON THE *OTHER*, IT'S ALL IN THE *INTERACTIONS*.

JUST A QUESTION OF HOW THEY *TALK* TO EACH OTHER, SO TO SPEAK.

CAN IT BE DONE WITHOUT ANYONE *KNOWING* WE'VE *DONE* IT?

THAT'S *DIFFERENT*. THE ABSENCE WOULD SHOW UP IN THE *LABS*, YOU'D NEED TO *SPOOF* THE BLOOD WORK, EITHER ON-SITE OR IN THE SYSTEM.

THIS IS *EVERYTHING* I COULD DOWNLOAD FROM SEQUOIA...

...SHOULD BE ENOUGH TO GET YOU **STARTED** BEFORE I CAN GET YOU **BACK** THERE.

IT SHOULD GO **WITHOUT** SAYING THAT THE **ONLY** PEOPLE WHO ARE TO KNOW ABOUT THIS ARE MYSELF, YOU, AND FOREVER.

YOU'RE ASKING ME TO COMMIT **TREASON.**

TREASON AGAINST THE FAMILY IS **DEATH.**

HOW CAN IT BE TREASON IF **I'M** THE ONE ASKING YOU TO **DO** IT, MICHAEL?

BECAUSE YOU DON'T WANT ANYONE **ELSE** TO KNOW.

Mhm. YOU'RE **RIGHT.**

IT'S **VERY** DANGEROUS, YOU KNOW THAT. FOR **BOTH** OF US.

WHICH MEANS WE'RE IN IT **TOGETHER,** MICHAEL. YOU DO **YOUR** PART, I'LL DO **MINE.**

WHY?

YOU KNOW THE ANSWER TO THAT.

NO, I MEAN, WHY DO YOU WANT TO DO THIS? WHAT'S THE *POINT*?

YOU *FREE* SONJA BITTNER, YOU FREE YOUR *SISTER*, TO WHAT *END*?

THAT *DOESN'T* CONCERN YOU.

IT *CONCERNS* ME IF I'M GOING TO *RISK* MY *LIFE* FOR IT.

I'M KEEPING A *PROMISE*.

"I UNDERSTAND THAT YOU AND JOHANNA HAD A TALK...

...I'M CURIOUS IF THAT MEANS YOU'RE NOW WILLING TO SPEAK TO *ME* AGAIN.

I DON'T KNOW WHAT TO SAY TO YOU.

TELL ME HOW YOU'RE *FEELING.*

FOOLISH.

WHY IS THAT?

I SAID THINGS TO YOU I CAN'T TAKE *BACK.*

I ACTED LIKE A *CHILD.*

NO, FOREVER, YOU WERE *HURT,* AND YOU HAD *EVERY* RIGHT TO BE. WHEN WE GET HURT, WE GET *ANGRY.*

I STAND BY WHAT I SAID. YOU ARE MY DAUGHTER, REGARDLESS OF *HOW* YOU CAME INTO THIS WORLD. BUT I SHOULD HAVE TOLD YOU THE *TRUTH* A LONG TIME AGO.

CAN YOU *FORGIVE* ME?

OF COURSE I CAN, FATHER.

YOU MAKE ME **VERY** PROUD, FOREVER.

I HOPE SO, SIR. I TRY TO.

I'LL LEAVE YOU TO IT...

...I KNOW YOU'RE ANXIOUS TO GET BACK INTO **ACTION.**

YOU, AH... YOU KNOW THAT **JOACQUIM MORRAY'S** BEEN DEPLOYED TO THE EUROPEAN THEATRE, YES?

I'VE BEEN READING THE BRIEFINGS. I SAW IT MENTIONED.

YOU TWO HAVE GROWN QUITE **CLOSE,** HAVEN'T YOU?

WE ARE... **FOND** OF EACH OTHER.

EVERYONE IS LOOKING AT NASSALOVKA RIGHT NOW, FOREVER, AND WITH **GOOD REASON.**

BUT DON'T TAKE THE MORRAY FAMILY FOR **GRANTED...**

...REGARDLESS OF HOW YOU **FEEL** ABOUT THEIR LAZARUS.

Four days ago

Stanford University
Family: Carlyle

--AS THE REQUEST CAME DIRECTLY FROM THE FAMILY...

Population [Serf]: 19,783

...I'M TO PROVIDE YOU WITH ANYTHING YOU MIGHT **NEED**, MICHAEL.

HOPEFULLY YOU'LL FIND THE FACILITIES TO YOUR **LIKING**, THOUGH I'M NOT **REALLY** CERTAIN WHAT YOU WERE GOING TO **NEED**...?

THIS'LL DO FINE, THANK YOU, DEAN MUHR.

I TRUST YOU'LL TELL THE FAMILY YOU THINK SO.

WHO IS THIS?

I WAS TOLD YOU'D NEED AN **ASSISTANT** FROM **OUTSIDE** THE GENETICS GROUP, PREFERABLY A **BIOCHEMIST**.

MICHAEL BARRETT.

CADY ROSALES.

THANK YOU, DEAN MUHR.

I'LL LET YOU KNOW IF I NEED ANYTHING **ELSE**.

WHAT'S YOUR FOCUS?

PRIMARILY AGRICULTURE.

CROPS?

YES.

WHAT ABOUT NEUROCHEMISTRY?

OR VIRUS CONSTRUCTION? SPECIFICALLY TO INHIBIT ELEMENTS OF THE GENOME?

NOT OUTSIDE SIRNA CONSTRUCTION AND IMPLEMENTATION.

BUT THAT'S CONFINED TO PLANTS.

YOU'RE... NEUROCHEMISTRY, YOU'RE TALKING ABOUT WORKING ON PEOPLE.

LET'S GET STARTED.

Three days ago

Puget Sound
Population [Family]: 3 [2 permanent]

...LOST CONTACT WITH THE O.P. OUTSIDE OF SULECIN AS OF TWO-FORTY-TWO LOCAL...

...DAGGER-BRAVO HAD QUICK-RESPONSE, WAS ON-SITE WITHIN **SEVEN** MINUTES OF THE ALERT.

THEY FOUND THE POST **DESTROYED**, EIGHTEEN **DEAD**, ANOTHER FOUR M.I.A.

CAPTURED?

MORE LIKELY THEY'RE DEAD, TOO.

THE BRUTALITY OF THE ZMEY CAN MAKE ESTABLISHING AN ACCURATE BODY COUNT **CHALLENGING.**

WE'VE GOT **UNCONFIRMED** SIGHTINGS PUTTING HIM AS FAR WEST AS FÜRSTENWALDE, AS FAR SOUTH AS PRAGUE.

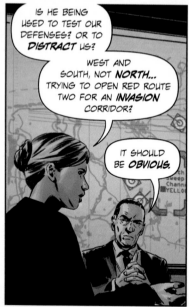

IS HE BEING USED TO TEST OUR DEFENSES? OR TO **DISTRACT** US?

WEST AND SOUTH, NOT **NORTH**... TRYING TO OPEN RED ROUTE TWO FOR AN **INVASION** CORRIDOR?

IT SHOULD BE **OBVIOUS.**

PERHAPS IF YOU **SHARED** YOUR PREDICTIVE **MODELS**, IT WOULD BE TO GENERAL VALERI AND I, AS WELL.

WOULD YOU **CARE** TO, FATHER? OR WOULD YOU RATHER WE JUST **GUESS**?

IT'S STRATEGIC **PROPAGANDA.**

VASSALOVKA'S CALLING OUR LAZARI **OUT.**

THE ZMEY'S ATTACKS WILL CONTINUE TO **ESCALATE,** COSTING US **MORE** IN LIVES AND MATERIEL, ALL THE WHILE UNDERMINING COALITION **MORALE.**

EVERY REPORT, EVERY ATTACK, EVERY ATTEMPT TO STOP HIM THAT **FAILS,** ALL WILL LET HIS **REPUTATION** GROW...

...WE ARE, IN FACT, BEING **USED** BY VASSALOVKA TO CREATE HIS **MONSTER.**

WE LOCATE HIM AND BOMB HIM BACK TO THE PRECAMBRIAN.

AND IF THAT **FAILS?** IF HE **SURVIVES** EVERYTHING WE THROW AT HIM, FROM BOMBS TO ARTILLERY?

WE WILL HAVE MADE HIM **INVINCIBLE.**

WE HAVE **THREE** LAZARI IN THE FIELD RIGHT NOW.

FOREVER COULD JOIN THEM WITHIN TWENTY-FOUR HOURS.

THAT'S **FOUR** LAZARI TO FACE ONE.

YES, IT IS. **FOUR** OF THEM IN THE SAME **PLACE.**

AT BEST, WE AND OUR ALLIES WILL HAVE COMMITTED OUR ARGUABLY **GREATEST** STRATEGIC RESOURCES TO DEAL WITH, ULTIMATELY, A **MINOR** STRATEGIC THREAT.

AND AT **WORST,** WE COULD COME OUT OF THIS HAVING LOST **ALL** OF THEM.

SHIT.

YOU'RE **HEAD OF FAMILY,** JOHANNA.

WHAT ARE **YOU** GOING TO **DO?**

Two days ago

CNb>zjNZ6rGvDaTh|~Dsqlnpy.JU0eN5LKsD?
AhGrL6i7F3sAoRV P{jPL8fxEAIH2HZKZ]
YDrSW7q]unWPLIfe"BiDECRYPTION_KEY_
IDENTIFIED_HANDSHAKE_ACCEPTED__
MESSAGE BEGINS

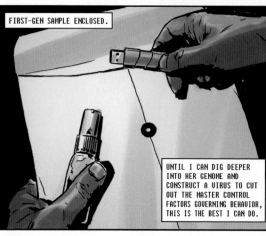

FIRST-GEN SAMPLE ENCLOSED.

UNTIL I CAN DIG DEEPER INTO HER GENOME AND CONSTRUCT A VIRUS TO CUT OUT THE MASTER CONTROL FACTORS GOVERNING BEHAVIOR, THIS IS THE BEST I CAN DO.

THIS IS STOP-GAP TREATMENT **ONLY.** IT GOES WITHOUT SAYING IT HASN'T BEEN TESTED.

FOR NOW, THOUGH, THIS SHOULD BE ENOUGH TO EFFECTIVELY "MUTE" THE RECEPTORS IN QUESTION.

SHE SHOULD SEE AN IMMEDIATE EFFECT, AND IF IT'S WORKING RIGHT, WON'T RAISE ANY FLAGS UNDER A SIMPLE BLOOD SCREEN.

I CANNOT STRESS THIS **ENOUGH**--

--THERE HAS BEEN **NO OPPORTUNITY TO TEST THIS.**

One day ago

IT MAY NOT EVEN WORK.

AND IF IT DOES WORK, IT LIKELY WON'T WORK FOR LONG.

LAST NOTE:

THIS TECHNIQUE SHOULD BE INVISIBLE UNDER CURSORY EXAM.

THAT SAID, IT **WILL** SHOW UP UNDER DETAILED BLOODWORK.

SO LET'S ALL HOPE THERE'S NO NEED FOR THAT.

I'LL KEEP AT IT UNTIL YOU SAY OTHERWISE.

HEMATOLOGY

THOMAS.

HULLO, FOREVER.

ACTION ON MY MARK.

I LOVE IT WHEN YOU TALK DIRTY.

IN THREE.

TWO.

ONE.

SINNED!

ACTION ACTION **ACTION!**

FLESH.

WILL.

BURN!

aah

Oh SHIT SHITSHIT--

SONJA! MOVE!

THOMAS!

JOACQUIM!

HIT HIM!

GORGON SIX, ACTUAL.

WE NEED EXFIL **NOW!**

ANIMAL... YOU--

WE'VE GOT TO GO.

WE **CAN'T** JUST--

WE'VE **LOST!**

WE'VE GOT TO GET **OUT** OF HERE...

FOREVER!

SEE.

YOU.

SOON.

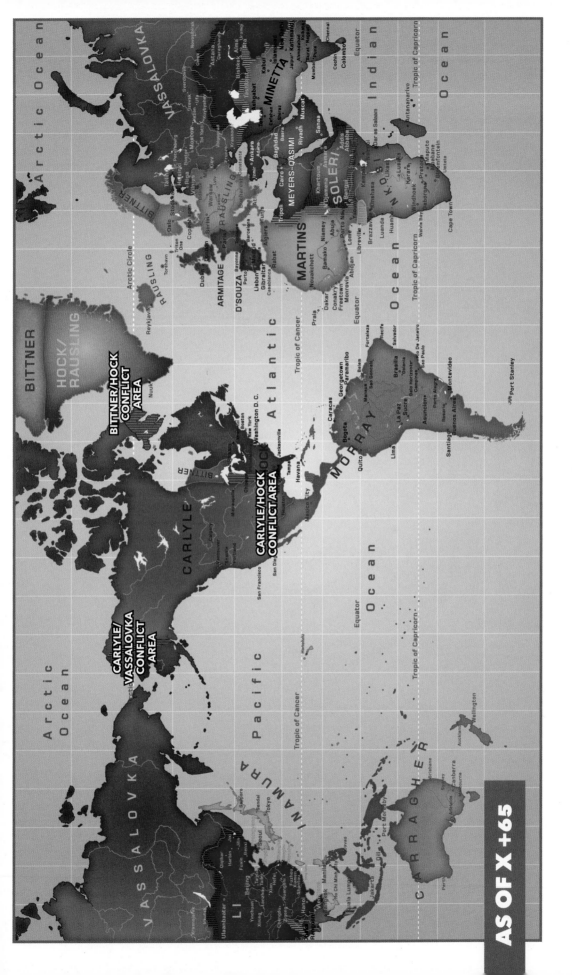

AS OF X +65

MICHAEL LARK

Michael Lark's variant cover for *Lazarus* #26, in honor of Women's History Month. The final piece featured the caption, "Nevertheless, she persisted."

FOR Oz - MLark

Art commission by Michael Lark, featuring Forever Carlyle and Sonja Bittner. From the collection of Oz Donald.

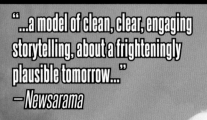

"...a model of clean, clear, engaging storytelling, about a frighteningly plausible tomorrow..."
— *Newsarama*

"The drama, intrigue and action that flows through **LAZARUS** is the best stuff going on in comics today."
— *Unleash The Fanboy*

LAZARUS ™

"... it's the kind of book that reminds fans just what great comics are capable of."
— *Comic Book Resources*

FROM IMAGE COMICS

image

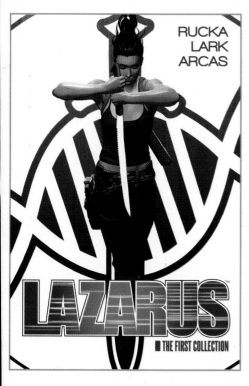
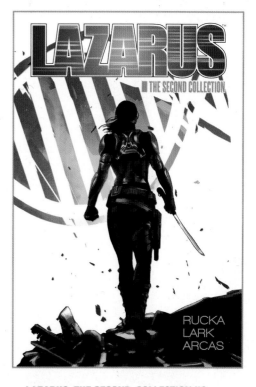
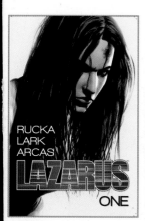